SAFFRON JACK

SAFFRON JACK

Rishi Dastidar

Nine
Arches
Press

Saffron Jack
Rishi Dastidar

ISBN: 978-1-911027-89-8
eISBN: 978-1-911027-90-4

First published March 2020 by:

Nine Arches Press
Unit 14, Sir Frank Whittle Business Centre,
Great Central Way, Rugby.
CV21 3XH
United Kingdom

www.ninearchespress.com

Nine Arches Press is supported using public funding
by Arts Council England.

Supported using public funding by
**ARTS COUNCIL
ENGLAND**

For my father

'As for me: I, too, like all migrants am a fantasist. I build imaginary countries and try to impose them on the ones that exist.'

– Salman Rushdie, *Shame*

In a small room, a border of masking tape. A demarcation down the middle.

The litter of the temporary sleeping space: a mattress, a desk. A TV, a lamp, a rucksack.

Stretched out, a body. Blue torso and yellow legs, bandaged in combat trousers and vest, desert boots. And a crown.

He sleeps, the head resting easy. Until alarm clock gunfire and an explosive sunrise scramble him awake.

Good morning tramper! Here's a loudhailer with your wake-up warning!

JULLIE HEBBEN EXACT ÉÉN UUR OM TE
VERTREKKEN, VÒÒR WE JULLIE LAND
BINNENVALLEN. JULLIE HEBBEN EXACT ÉÉN
UUR OM TE VERTREKKEN, VÒÒR WE JULLIE
LAND BINNENVALLEN. LAAT ALLES ACHTER.
NEEM NIETS MEE. JULLIE HEBBEN EXACT ÉÉN
UUR OM TE VERTREKKEN, VÒÒR WE JULLIE
LAND BINNENVALLEN.

VOUS AVEZ UNE HEURE POUR PARTIR AVANT
QUE NOUS N'ENVAHISSIONS VOTE PAYS.
VOUS AVEZ UNE HEURE POUR PARTIR AVANT
QUE NOUS N'ENVAHISSIONS VOTRE PAYS.
LAISSEZ TOUT. NE PRENEZ RIEN. VOUS AVEZ
UNE HEURE POUR PARTIR AVANT QUE NOUS
N'ENVAHISSIONS VOTRE PAYS.

YOU HAVE ONE HOUR TO LEAVE, BEFORE WE
INVADE YOUR COUNTRY. YOU HAVE ONE HOUR
TO LEAVE, BEFORE WE INVADE YOUR COUNTRY.
LEAVE EVERYTHING. TAKE NOTHING. YOU
HAVE ONE HOUR TO LEAVE, BEFORE WE
INVADE YOUR COUNTRY.

STOP.

Tense, nervous fingers fidget around, feeling the crown.
Remembering, confirming it is his. Sealed and not sutured.

Now cuticles on the end of pipecleaners work their way up a
little more to find the clunk of a metallic open-top hat-band.

It is not a dream.

1. You polish it every night.

>1.1. No, not that.

>1.2. The crown.

>>1.2.1. Every night.

2. It's the only way.

>2.1. A bit of spit and whatever is to hand. Sometimes just your hand.

>>2.1.1. What you are wearing.

>2.2. It seems to do the trick.

3. Even at the end, you must maintain appearances, the trappings of office.

>3.1. Otherwise, what do you have left?

>3.2. Yes, it is only symbolic.

>>3.2.1. Yes, you are only symbolic.

>3.3. But it is what is left. What you have left.

>3.4. And they're not taking that away. Not now.

>3.5. Not yet.

4. You didn't think it would end like this.

    4.1. But then, no one ever does.

        4.1.1. Divine rights and inviolate.

    4.2. You get used to being told the position you hold is immortal.

5. By sleight of mind, you come to believe the same.

    5.1. That you are immortal.

    5.2. Because position and person are one and the same.

        5.2.1. As vested in you, represented by you.

6. So they cannot ever touch you, no matter the screw ups you make.

6.1. Because they are not mistakes.

6.2. They are whimsical unpredictabilities with a happy effect; keeping consort and court, mistresses and subjects, on their toes.

6.3. It is not that you are never wrong – who possesses the temerity or sheer bad manners to whisper that to you?

6.3.1. To your face?

6.4. No matter the pattern of choices – some sort of internal coherency can always be found.

6.5. A chain of logic that is clear, and followable.

6.5.1. (Even if 'followable' isn't a word.)

6.6. Even if it is irrational to the outside eye.

6.7. Even if it is irrational.

6.8. Because what does the outside eye know?

6.9. Blinded by the gilded edges of the caravan.

6.10. Always confusing the trappings for substance.

7. Not that the trappings are not substantial.

    7.1. Or not necessary.

        7.1.1. They are a feint. A distraction.

        7.1.2. Be dazzled enough by the shiny shiny, you won't ask why everything is only being held by a few pieces of tape and string.

    7.2. Though someone comes along one day, and says,

        7.2.1. 'Look, look, I can see some rust!'

8. And then it is all over.

9. Not immediately.

10. You keep the motions of the pretence up.

> 10.1. Blinding the rust-spotters, the string-cutters, the tape-slicers.

> 10.2. Silencing those who say the rust-spotters, the string-cutters, the tape-slicers should have their say, and keep saying it.

> 10.3. Imprisoning those who say that the advice is not bad and should be listened to.

> 10.4. Sending into exile those who suggest you need new advisers –

>> 10.4.1. advisers who should look like, sound like, the people suggesting you need new advisers.

11. Dismissing and diminishing until the only evidence you are actually who you say you are is a piece of tarnished metal.

12. And your unshakeable belief in the purity of your bloodline.

> 12.1. However diluted it might be.

13. By then, no doubt, the wars have started.

13.1. Because you have given enough hostages to fortune, caused enough noses to be broken out of joint.

13.1.1. Made sure enough interests are not vested.

13.2. Sure, it is dressed up as something patriotic, noble, for country and 'crown' –

13.2.1. whatever that is.

13.3. A naked attempt to try and preserve something nebulous.

13.4. The moment you cannot guarantee status, for you and all your people, you are done.

13.4.1. You.

13.4.2. Are.

13.4.3. Done.

13.5. And you have made sure you cannot.

13.6. Because you cannot take a decision without pissing someone off.

14. A grudge, always against you.

> 14.1. A grudge, with easy access to a caché of weapons.

>> 14.1.1. Better than yours.

> 14.2. The claque you were relying on for your guns and bodies are those now in front of you.

>> 14.2.1. Surrounding you.

15. You are a king. Until someone points a gun at you.

> 15.1. Majesty disappears like dew in the morning when confronted with an AK-47.

16. It is not that you set out to become one. This.

> 16.1. Become this.

> 16.2. It just happened.

> 16.3. And you are most comfortable being it. Wearing these clothes.

> 16.4. Who hasn't put on a toy crown, and wished it real?

17. You tried being different types of leader.

    17.1. A director. Then a managing one.

    17.2. You got the corporate vogue.

    17.3. Chief Executive Officer.

    17.4. Thrusting. Heft. Modern.

        17.4.1. Big.

        17.4.2. Big initials.

            17.4.2.1. Big balls.

18. But you tired of fronting a corporation. You *grandeur* more than that.

    18.1. So a First Minister. Then a Prime Minister.

        18.1.1. *Primus inter pares*.

    18.2. Even a President, for a bit – why not?

    18.3. You weren't wedded to any idea of how you should rule.

        18.3.1. Just that *you* should.

19. It could have been through other means. Other people.

    19.1. As long as you were the other person who mattered more, mattered most.

    19.2. Who lied to themselves better than anyone else.

20. You should have gone for a cult of personality.

    20.1. Some extreme narcissism to go with your incipient megalomania.

    20.2. But you don't look good in bronze or stone.

        20.2.1. No profile for statuary.

            20.2.1.1. Do not have the cheekbones.

21. It was never actually about the spoils.

> 21.1. How can it be, when you start your own country from scratch?
>
>> 21.1.1. Your own imagined country.
>
> 21.2. No ill-gotten loot that needed laundering.
>
> 21.3. Or independent means that needed frittering.
>
>> 21.3.1. No pissing off mummy and the trustees.

22. There is not much money in this business, not outside the key markets.

> 22.1. The ones with lots of loyal subjects, who look at you with adoring eyes whenever you pass them in the street, all stretched out in your national champion limo –

>> 22.1.1. You could never commit such a *faux pas* as to be driven around in your real ride, because it comes from Wolfsburg or Turin or Mumbai.

>> 22.1.2. Not where you are.

>>> 22.1.2.1. Where these goofs live, the credulous live.

>> 22.1.3. These places where they are happy to be 'subjects'.

>>> 22.1.3.1. And they don't have the wit to realise that it means to be 'subjugated' too.

23. You do not get into the kingship racket to make a fast buck.

> 23.1. There are better ways to make some money –

>> 23.1.1. or a living

>>> 23.1.1.1. or to stay alive.

24. This one gave you a lot of freedom –

    24.1. at the expense of other people

        24.1.1. sorry, *subjects*

        24.1.2. maybe.

    24.2. It was well past time you took a bit of freedom

        24.2.1. for you.

    24.3. Because if you didn't

        24.3.1. no one else would do it for you.

He takes his crown off his head.

He worries it around with his fingers.

25. How much was this crown?

25.1. This proof and reproof of your status?

25.2. It is not a question you thought you might ask, when you were at school.

25.3. What happens when you need to buy a crown?

25.3.1 And you do not mean a tiara.

25.3.1.1. (You're not on your hen night.

25.3.1.2. Much as you might wish you were…)

25.4. You mean a proper, *fuck off I'm a king* crown.

25.4.1. (John Lewis don't stock them.

25.4.1.1. Not even Peter Jones.

25.4.1.2. The last piece of evidence the shops were founded by a Marxist.

25.4.1.3. 'My apologies, sir, we've never had a royal headwear department.')

26. Why go where every other monarch has gone before you?

27. Elizabeth Duke.

    27.1. As your royal jewellers by warrant.

        27.1.1. It wasn't your first choice.

28. A crown helicoptered in specially.

    28.1. Now the only thing you'll be able to take with you.

    28.2. The last relic of your reign.

    28.3. The only relic of your reign.

    28.4. Not many monarchies will leave a lighter footprint than yours.

29. You would love to stuff your pockets with jewels and dubloons, wine and old masters and furs and silks; whatever you are meant to do – to claim as yours – when the curtain is coming down. A hogshead or two. But no.

30. All you have left is a cheap shit, £9.99 crown from Argos.

    30.1. And a little blue pen.

        30.1.1. 'Order No. SJ33, please come to the collection point.'

And a hedera falls off the page.

❧

31. You consider whether the audience might be forgiven for being confused.

>31.1. 'He's brown. Brown people can't be king.'

>>31.1.2. 'Can they?'

>31.2. 'Maybe where they come from, they can be kings there? They come from places that still have kings, don't they?'

>>31.2.1. 'All the glitzy turbans in the Raj, they were princes or mararajahs anyway.'

>>31.2.2. 'Oh, but wasn't Victoria the Empress, so she outranked them all.'

>>31.2.3. 'But didn't we give them our democracy and shit, so there wouldn't be any more kings?'

>>31.2.4. 'So what's he doing here with a crown on his head, pretending to be one?'

32. Good question.

33. You are not sure how you got here either.

> 33.1. But before you tell that story, you should say where 'here' is.

>> 33.1.1. For all you live-action battlefield tourists.

34. What you see, that's just the *appearance*. What something looks like. Not the truth.

> 34.1. Your eyes don't tell you what's true.

> 34.2. Remember – it's the *lie* of the land.

>> 34.2.1. You find the real story under the contours of the map.

35. A map unrolled from the heavens, swamping you in topography.

36. So, before the fighting started –

36.1. entirely predictably, by the way –

36.1.1. two over-proud and under-clever populations rubbing each other up the wrong way for three-quarters of a millennium.

36.2. This little ol' hamlet where I'm now reigning had been a governmental nightmare.

36.2.1. A continental oddity.

36.2.1.1. An administrative anomaly.

36.2.1.2. A legalistic fuck-up.

37. It's hard to see why. It's hard to see much here.

37.1. Some squares that mean something to someone.

37.1.1. A few coloured lines making a collection of villages.

37.2. Or maybe a power play.

37.3. An aborted archipelago, that forgot where the sea was.

37.4. The dangers of irrational geography.

38. What do you see here?

    38.1. The future history of humanity.

    38.2. One endless, individual bun fight.

39. It was – was – a town where two countries intertwined.

    39.1. Not met, but mixed.

    39.2. One house was in one country.

        39.2.1. The neighbours in another.

    39.3. No joke.

    39.4. One door, Crazyland.

        39.4.1. Next door Barmylandia.

            39.4.1.1. Not that I can call them that any more.

            39.4.1.2. Because somebody will shoot me

            39.4.1.3. for being an insult of a neighbour.

        39.4.2. And yes, in some of the houses a border right through the bathroom too.

40. Three thousand people, living as two.

41. Or they were.

    41.1. With double of everything.

    41.2. Many secretaries of foreign tongues.

    41.3. Two traditions, both heartfelt, both ridiculous.

    41.4. Two churches, two schools.

    41.5. Two town halls for parading past.

    41.6. Two sets of lights, road signs, post boxes.

    41.7. Electrics, telephone systems, even double drains.

        41.7.1. Twin natural monopoly fun.

    41.8. Two lots of media, because a uniform babble wasn't enough.

42. Each side its own newspaper too.

>42.1. Each used to be content to stir the pot,

>>42.1.1. to keep things a little spicy, entertaining.

>42.2. But that was before 'prevailing economic imperatives' meant things had to get hotter.

>42.3. War sells papers, they thought.

>>42.3.1. That they weren't wrong about. Pity it wasn't a long-term redoubt.

43. Like they'd been planning for it, two sets of policemen became two armies.

>43.1. Small armies, sure.

>43.2. But when you've got a grenade without a pin at your feet, who's counting the infantry wandering past?

44. Everyone pasted their particular allegiance on their front door,

>44.1. the good citizens, the loyal citizens, patriotic citizens.

>44.2. So it wasn't hard for the opposing team to find them,

>>44.2.1. deal with them.

45. A gap in the crack of history.

46. No one steamrollered these little parcels of land, these little statelets into one empire's pancake.

> 46.1. If you wait long enough, they'll do it themselves.

> 46.2. Can't tear each other apart fast enough.

47. That's friction for you.

> 47.1. Enough of it, the conflagration inevitable.

> 47.2. Sparks, everywhere you look.

48. Everything central, but peripheral, all at the same time.

49. The memories too.

50. People tried to die on the right side of the line.

>50.1. They did not want to ascend to the wrong heaven.

>50.2. Corpses dragged through the streets, over the different paving stones, so they had done their duty by their patrie.

>>50.2.1. That their god knew that they had been true.

51. Why tip up in a war zone?

>51.1. You are no adrenalin junkie;

>51.2. You do not want to shed any red stuff.

>>51.2.1. It is not your fight

>>51.3. but you spot a chance like the next man.

>51.4. Localised carnage is some of best opportunity hunting you can get.

52. You can slip between the cracks unnoticed

>52.1. until you *want* to be noticed.

>52.2. What is one small, brown face?

>52.3. Exactly.

53. So you have come to this discrepancy.

    53.1. To start something here.

    53.2. Another discrepancy.

54. A country fit for you.

55. You had the idea on the train.

56. Yes, you know you should have arrived in a manner more romantic, befitting your soon-to-be-really-true-this-time status as an outcast.

    56.1. A romantic in exile, a successful runner-awayer

    56.2. from all the stuff that was so bad that you couldn't stay and fix it.

57. It'd suit you – and your story – more if you'd used a mode of transport more exotic.

    57.1. A trampsteamer.

        57.1.1. Something to weather-beat you.

    57.2. Che had his motorcycle trip, where heroes were found, destinies forged, myths made.

    57.3. You? You had the Eurostar.

        57.3.1. Your heroism stretching as far as trying to sneak champagne from first class.

        57.3.2. Stuck in the tunnel for hours 'due to the inclement conditions at Calais'.

            57.3.2.1. The condition are always inclement at Calais.

        57.3.3. One couple so bored, they started the Mile-Below Club.

            57.3.3.1. You didn't have that distraction available to you – maybe if you had, more regularly… okay, at all… growing up, maybe you might be calmer than you are now…

58. With nothing else to do but look out at the wall holding back the sea, you drifted.

58.1. You drifted to being younger,

58.1.1. bank holidays at home, the rain, the inside, the couch, in front of the TV,

58.1.1.1. hoping that instead of the Bond, whatever was left over in Disney's cupboard, there would actually be something else on.

58.1.1.2. Something interesting. Something different.

58.2. And this one time, there was.

59. A bang on the TV. A splutter into life. And then on it

59.1. *The Man Who Would Be King*.

60. *"For it's a nation I shall make of 'em with a flag and an anthem and a standing Army!... I'll treat with the Viceroy on equal terms – and other Kings and Princes... And, when I've accomplished what I set out to do, I'll stand one day before the Queen – not kneel, mind you, but stand like an equal – and she'll say, 'I'd like you to accept the Order of the Garter as a mark of my esteem, Cousin'... And she'll pin it on me herself. Oh, it's big. It's big, I tell you!"*

61. A jolly in the sub-continent

    61.1. when the sub-continent was ours –

    61.2. no, theirs –

        61.2.1. to be jollied.

62. Two mad-dog Englishmen, short on high Victorian imperial boredom, long on chutzpah and capers

    62.1. smuggle some guns into some country.

        62.1.1. The Kafiristan Job.

    62.2. Then some cunning, some chance, some shooting

    62.3. and one of them ends up running the show.

    62.4. The locals reckon he's the Son, and they all start bowing down to him.

        62.4.1. Just like that.

63. And you thought, wouldn't that be bloody cool. Well, not just to be Sean Connery, that obviously would be bloody cool. But. You know, it'd also be cool to just control somewhere, especially a somewhere when you've felt that you've never fitted in wherever the where is you're from. And then have loads of people suddenly decide that, yes, despite the fact that you look different, sound different, talk different, and scare them with your guns and what have you, still you're a better bet than the current fat nabob they have, who goes around taking their bread from them, their grain from them, their money from them, taking their wives and daughters from them whenever he fancies, with only a little bit of prompting and cajoling, a twinkling smile or two which they understand even if they don't understand what the smile is saying; they take that and the guns and the weapons and the drill and the tactics and the confidence you've given them, and they surround the fat nabob's palace in a ring of chanting, heaving, determined bodies which won't shift, and if he tried to sneak through he'd get sucked into a maw of flesh like being sucked into a whirlpool, so the nabob's got no other choice but to give in and throw his hands up, throw his crown up, his queen up, and when he looks round at who to give them to so he isn't torn into pieces the size of the stamps with his fat head on them, and the crowd are growling and shuffling and getting ready to start pitching sharp things at him, it's only when he looks at you with the crown in one hand and imploring gesture being made by the other, and his

eyes are watery and pleading and hopeful and hopeless and scared, and the crowd suddenly hush as they see where he's looking, and you suddenly feel your arm lifting and your hand reaching out and you gently trace the band of the crown once round to make sure it is real, and then you close the whole of your hand around it, and you snatch it with a jerk, and look at it in the same way you looked at her when she slowly undressed that night in your room and then before anyone can do anything, take anything away, you put the crown on your head, pretending you're not being reverential (but you are a bit), trying to be that cocky and cool person that all the people down there have been inspired by, and now should be slightly scared of, and then there's a moment of pure, utter silence like you get at 4am, when everything is still or dead, and then you're almost blown back by this gust or noise, this *rush* of love and fear and hope and expectations and dreams, all in this one blast, this one *expansion* of emotion.

64. Yeah, that'd be cool.

    64.1. Yeah, that'd be fucking cool.

65. And you remembered that on the train –

    65.1. that feeling of fucking coolness.

    65.2. And you remembered you'd wanted some of that then

        65.2.1. and then it hit you with the force of what would be a biblical revelation

            65.2.1.1. (if you believed in biblical revelations)

        65.2.2. that you still did, you really did, and that you shouldn't have let yourself slip away from that dream.

            65.2.2.1. Or was it that you didn't work hard enough, and do what you needed to do to make sure you got there?

    65.3. But this time, this now, it wasn't hazy at all.

    65.4. And what was clearer than anything else was the notion that you had been right:

    65.5. that you should have tried to get some of that action, and now was the time to change that

        65.5.1. and get into the monarchy racket.

66. You decided you would become a king.

67. Now what?

Another breath, another breath.

❧

68. It's one thing to think it

> 68.1. to say it to yourself
>
> 68.2. then maybe a whisper
>
>> 68.2.1. under your breath
>
> 68.3. then quietly
>
> 68.4. then louder
>
> 68.5. then louder
>
> 68.6. then louder still
>
> 68.7. then louder again
>
> 68.8. louder and louder and louder
>
> 68.9. until it echoes down the carriage
>
> 68.10. until it ricochets out into the sea:

69. 'I WILL BE A KING!'

70. But how do you do it?

> 70.1. You have not been born into it, so you cannot inherit a gig.
>
> 70.2. You don't see the job advertised either:
>
>> 70.2.1. 'One throne, plenty of other owners, now needs filling – it could be you!'
>
> 70.3. Can you imagine, at jobcentreplus:
>
> 70.4. *'Have you applied for any jobs this week?'*
>
>> *'Yeah.'*
>>
>> *'What sort of jobs?'*
>>
>> *'King ones.'*
>>
>> *'What do you mean?'*
>>
>> *'Y'know, jobs where you can be a king.'*
>>
>> *'I didn't know we actually had any of those.'*
>>
>> *'No, not that many. I've been keeping my eyes open and everything.'*
>>
>> *'Have you tried working at the warehouse?'*
>>
>> *'What does a warehouse want with a king?*

71. And so the welfare state crumbles a little more.

72. No, if you are going to be a king, you can't sit around

    72.1. waiting

        72.1.1. for a kingdom to open up for you.

73. You are going to have to do it yourself.

    73.1. Which means one of two things.

74. Invasion.

    74.1. Or starting your own country.

75. And after years of waiting, your dumb luck turned

    75.1. so you could do one

    75.2. vicariously experience the other.

76. Not that you had anything to do with it kicking off, wherever you are.

76.1. (And now, you just shrug at the gunfire.)

77. You didn't know this place existed.

77.1. You got off the train, no idea of what to do next.

77.2. Jumped into a taxi, asked to go somewhere 'interesting'.

77.2.1. You meant 'close by'.

77.2.2. Trust you to get a cab driver with an unused PhD in International Relations

77.2.3. rehearsing his viva –

A sudden, persistent beeping. A mobile phone. The screen glows news.

YOU HAVE LESS THAN ONE HOUR
TO LEAVE, BEFORE WE INVADE YOUR
COUNTRY. YOU HAVE LESS THAN ONE
HOUR TO LEAVE, BEFORE WE INVADE
YOUR COUNTRY. LEAVE EVERYTHING.
TAKE NOTHING.

STOP.

78. Just a text.

> 78.1. A text.

> 78.2. Are you not enough of a king to be sent more than a SMS?

>> 78.2.1. Where are the men with sashes and halberds? Why haven't they rushed you yet? You are just an irritant to them, a deluded goof, unrespected.

>>> 78.2.1.1. Too busy fighting each other. Or obeying the rules of war. Some heartening proprieties remain.

79. Oh yes, where were you?

> 79.1. In the taxi.

>> 79.1.1. It was not a short journey.

>> 79.1.2. Cabbie's 'interesting' was not *quite* yours.

> 79.2. You have never had a burning desire to tip up in a war zone.

>> 79.2.1. And you should have asked how much –

>>> 79.2.1.1. no tip, after tipping up.

80. And then, here you were.

81. And now, here you still are.

82. You are not a violent person.

>82.1. You do not, you never did go, looking for aggravation, any excuse for a ruck.

>82.2. You shrink from fists.

>82.3. Fighting does not make you a man.

>>82.3.1. It makes less of you, by having the tendency of killing you.

>>82.3.2. There cannot be any less of you than that.

83. So the obvious thing would be to turn tail.

> 83.1. Double back and be done with it.

>> 83.1.1. Stick out a thumb, scramble into a van.

>> 83.1.2. Trudge trudge trudge away.

>> 83.1.3. Whatever to get the hell out of here and have anecdotes to tell, about how you survived combat operations.

>>> 83.1.3.1. They don't need to know how long for.

84. But then you begin thinking that you might be being over-hasty.

> 84.1. Sure, it was not your first choice.

>> 84.1.1. But there have to be some *opportunities*.

> 84.2. A war doesn't just need the mindlessly brave;

>> 84.2.1. it wants the cunningly cowardly too.

>> 84.2.2. A role you were over-qualified for.

85. A crisis should never be wasted, as the wisdom has it.

    85.1. Even if it has nothing to do with you.

    85.2. One intervention always leads to another.

    85.3. So the question became: what can you do now that you are here?

86. It hit you. You remembered.

87. Your idea. You can have it here.

    87.1. Your little project. Your big plan.

    87.2. Your little statelet. Your big society.

    87.3. Your kingdom. Your world.

88. It's not as easy as you think.

    88.1. Starting one of these.

    88.2. Whatever one of these is.

        88.2.1. A country, a canton, a bantustan.

89. You did not have a clue.

>89.1. Why would you? Why would anyone have a clue?

>89.2. Most people are happy where they are.

>>89.2.1. With what they are born into.

>89.3. The way things are set up.

>>89.3.1. That's how most people want to keep things.

90. Well, most of the people with any form of power at any rate.

91. Of course, they, the people with any form of power, don't follow their own logic.

91.1. Separate people out, make them atomised.

91.1.1. Keep telling everyone that they're unique.

91.1.1.1. An individual.

91.1.2. That they matter, truly matter, more than nearly anyone else,

91.1.2.1. except a few blood ties and maybe the other name on a marriage certificate, and that is it.

92. Now, why would you then be surprised if some of the –

92.1. how shall you say –

92.1.1. more impressionable amongst you

92.2. might believe it,

92.2.1. start to embroider it,

92.2.2. start to make that tale, that narrative,

92.2.3. a little more dramatic –

92.2.3.1. and take it to the obvious conclusion.

93. That every man, every woman can, should be, their own island.

    93.1. Yes, John Donne, you heard.

94. Every man, every woman can, should be, their own island.

94.1. Their own tax haven.

94.2. Don't like the laws you happen to have been born under?

94.2.1. Find some more amenable ones.

94.2.2. And what can be more amenable than rules that you've made up yourself, for you to obey, in a manner of your choosing?

94.2.2.1. This one sure, this one, not so much.

94.2.2.1.1. Better change that one.

94.2.2.2. The only person you are answerable to is you.

95. Any decent manual for starting up your own country

> 95.1. isn't all that straightforward to come by.
>
> 95.2. Obviously you should have done some research before you left.
>
> 95.3. But you've never been that sort of traveller.
>
>> 95.3.1. Turn up, wing it, see what you see, you know?
>>
>> 95.3.2. Alas, that's only going to get you so far.
>>
>>> 95.3.2.1. Need to be a bit more robust.

96. Which meant –

> 96.1. apart from learning how to duck all the incoming –
>
> 96.2. seeing if you could get your hands on a how-to guide, a dummies book.
>
> 96.3. Again, your luck was in.
>
>> 96.3.1. Apparently these fighters are sensitive, literate types.
>>
>> 96.3.2. The bookshop had not been touched.

A rummage inside the rucksack. A book he's almost in love with.

97. That was enough to get you started.

98. That there *actually* was a how-to guide.

> 98.1. Well, not *actually* a how-to guide.

> 98.2. But someone had bothered to go round, document all the attempts people had made at cocking a snook at the existing nations.

> 98.3. And thereby discovered the things you need – officially – to be a country.

>> 98.3.1. You quote directly from the book:

>> 98.3.2. 'According to the 1933 Montevideo Convention on the Rights and Duties of States, a nation needs only four things to exist:

>>> 98.3.2.1. a permanent population;

>>> 98.3.2.2. a defined territory;

>>> 98.3.2.3. a government;

>>> 98.3.2.4. and the capacity to enter into relationships with other states.'

99. It had a bit of advice from Frank Zappa too.

> 99.1. He reckoned that all your country really needs is:

>> 99.1.1. beer;

>> 99.1.2. an airline;

>> 99.1.3. some nuclear weapons;

>> 99.1.4. and a football team.

>>> 99.1.4.1. The beer's the most important.

100. Here is the really crazy thing. You don't need to be recognised

> 100.1. by anyone else – any other country.

> 100.2. Oh sure, all the other nations, whatever, ignore you.

>> 100.2.1. But fuck them.

> 100.3. You can say it, and it is true.

101. "I am a country."

102. The Declarative Theory of Statehood.

>102.1. *"L'État, c'est moi."*

>>102.1.1. Literally.

103. So why fuck somebody else's country up? Just make your own!

>103.1. It's a growth market! Everyone is at it.

>103.2. A veritable geopolitical gold rush.

>103.3. Since 1990, they reckon there has been about thirty-three new ones.

>>103.3.1. And it is going up.

>103.4. Just sit through an Olympics opening ceremony.

>>103.4.1. That parade never ends.

104. And they consider themselves 'proper countries', too.

>104.1. Now what they are is mostly the runt offspring of war, rebellions, ethnic fissures finally imploding, that sorta thing.

>>104.1.1. Created out of little more than thin air and an inflated sense of grievance.

105. But if you had invented a Do-It-Yourself-nation-flat-pack kit, you would have been raking it in.

106. No wonder people have wanted to get in on the action.

106.1. Look at some of the names.

106.1.1. The Republic of Rose Island.

106.1.2. Libertocracy.

106.1.3. Atlantium.

106.1.4. The Kingdom of TorHaven.

106.1.5. Nova Roma.

106.1.6. The Principality of Freedonia.

106.1.7. Freestonia.

106.1.8. Greenia.

106.1.9. Elleore. Akhzivland. Molossia.

106.1.10. The Republic of Kugelmugel.

106.1.11. The Principality of Vikesland.

106.1.12. The Kingdom of Romkerhall.

106.1.13. The Ibrosian Protectorate.

106.1.14. Westarcticca. Borovnia.

106.1.15. Rathnelly. Saugeis. Caux.

106.1.16. The Hutt River nation.

106.1.17. The province of Bumbumga.

106.1.18. The Duchy of Avram.

106.1.19. Rainbow Creek. United Oceania.

106.1.20. The Principality of Ponderosa.

107. The Great Republic of Rough and Ready.

107.1. Who would not want to live in The Great Republic of Rough and Ready?

107.2. That is a patriotism you want to see.

107.2.1. You might even be tempted to die for that flag.

108. Australia. They are always doing it there.

108.1. They do it more than anybody else.

108.1.1. That is where you want your DIY kit.

108.2. Maybe it is due to the blood they have.

108.2.1. Endlessly, restlessly rebellious.

108.2.2. Unquelled spirits and all that.

108.3. And all that land.

108.3.1. Wide expanses of orange land, all waiting to be filled.

108.3.1.1. '…What, there were people there before? *Really?*

108.3.1.1.1. You're so funny…'

108.3.2. Low state pension? Ardent monarchist? Disgruntled farmer? Colonial re-enactor?

108.3.2.1. Does not matter. Just kick up some dust, and create your own.

108.3.2.2. And they do.

108.4. Running away from the reality of whatever shit their lives might have given them.

109. All a new utopia.

    109.1. In somebody's head at least.

110. They are even making land now.

    110.1. Airports perch on reclaimed guano.

    110.2. Celebrity beach villas rise out of the sparkling coral blue in superficially benign petro-emirates.

111. You really can do this too.

    111.1. You do not have to fear seceding from wherever you happen to have your temporary or permanent allegiance,

        111.1.1. whatever woman you have planted your flag into.

    111.2. Want to be king? Just throw enough dirt in the sea,

        111.2.1. and you too can put a roll of tinfoil on your head and get others to call you sire.

112. You should be warned.

> 112.1. These things have a fast turnover, a high burnout rate.

> 112.2. People do not like it when someone who not a moment before was an equal, suddenly takes airs and graces upon themselves.

> 112.3. Declares themselves all higher, mightier than everyone else.

>> 112.3.1. It brings the critics out.

>>> 112.3.1.1. The law. The guns.

>>> 112.3.1.2. For a hobby, a pastime, that is some pretty crazy shit to be dealing with.

113. But you know. Or you should know. This is not a hobby. This is everything.

Get ready to go again.

❧

114. So you have to set the thing up.

    114.1. Your country.

        114.1.1. Your land of milk and honey.

            114.1.1.1. Your *heimat* for one.

115. If you had had a blank sheet of paper, and a blank strip of land

    115.1. you might have thought more about the aesthetics of the place.

        115.1.1. Whether it's bare or grassy.

        115.1.2. Marshy or arid.

            115.1.2.1. Rutted scrubland under lowering skies.

            115.1.2.2. Or verdant pastures under the softening sun.

116. If you cannot dream when you are doing this, when can you?

>116.1. If you cannot play God when you are doing this, when can you?

>116.2. Play.

>>116.2.1. We do not play enough any more?

>>116.2.2. Just think of this all as one giant playtime,

>>>116.2.2.1. and it will all be fine –

And guns fire in agreement.

117. To find your playground.

>117.1. Find somewhere inspiring. Find somewhere beautiful.

>117.2. Find somewhere to take the breath away.

>>117.2.1. Find somewhere –

More guns come out to play.

YOU WERE GOING TO SAY SAFE, BUT LET'S
BE HONEST HERE.

YOU WILL START BEING HONEST NOW.

YOU HAVE TO START BEING HONEST NOW.

STOP.

117.2.2. plenty of quixotic ideas that have gone on to greater things have had less noble beginnings than this.

118. Why can't a country start in the barely still-standing shell of a one-room shack?

118.1. Everywhere needs its creation myth.

118.2. This is yours. This is yours.

A hand is stuck into the rucksack and emerges with a sceptre. And then a walk – a procession – begins around the walls of the room. The sceptre is banged down rhythmically, regularly.

Thump.

Thump.

Thump.

119. This is beating the bounds.

    119.1. Your bounds.

    119.2. The human equivalent of pissing on the ground if you are a wolf.

        119.2.1. Territory marking. Nothing more sinister than that.

120. Halfway round completing this action, you realised

    120.1. what you were blessing into being lacked a name.

        120.1.1. That could not stand.

    120.2. What sort of oath of loyalty could you take

    120.3. without something ringingly patriotic

        120.3.1. to bellow at the top of your lungs?

121. Beware nominative determinism.

121.1. You did not want to jinx yourself with a handle

121.1.1. that foretold something bleak.

121.1.2. Or that boxed you into a future that was not of your choosing.

121.1.3. Geography is destiny, do not forget.

121.1.3.1. Napoleon, that one.

121.1.3.1.1. Clever fella.

121.2. And then, like all the best inspiration does.

121.2.1. Out of nowhere.

122. Cockaigne.

122.1. Cockaigne.

122.2. Cockaigne,

122.3. Cockaigne, Cockaigne.

122.4. Cockaigne. Cockaigne. Cockaigne. Cockaigne. Cockaigne.

123. You rolled it around your mouth for hours.

>123.1. 'An imaginary land of luxury and idleness'.

>>123.1.1. Sounds good, doesn't it?

>123.2. A fabulous place. A fabled place.

>>123.2.1. Where the food falls directly into your mouth.

>>123.2.2. Where the honey runs through your hands, where it rains milk,

>>123.2.3. where there is plenty of the easy you have always wanted.

>>>123.2.3.1. Total self-indulgence. In one handy country-sized bundle.

124. What more could a son want from life?

124.1. You are a firstborn. Feted, spoilt. Pandered to.

124.2. Your mother giving you everything you wanted between the ages of zero to thirty.

124.2.1. And that makes you weak.

124.2.2. Unable to survive outside a comforting bosom.

124.3. A little prince, who wants the privileges of birth to carry on forever.

124.3.1. Full-time royalty forever.

124.4. And who shall you be today?

124.4.1. Scourge of God.

124.4.2. The Strong to Aid, Exalted be the Standard.

124.4.3. Transformer of the Earth.

124.4.4. Universal Ruler.

124.4.5. The Prince Leaving Bengal Lights in His Wake.

124.4.6. The Bey of This Temporary Autonomous Zone.

124.4.7. The Very Lonely One, The One Set Apart.

124.4.8. Prototype Martyr of the Jelly Baby Heart.

124.4.9. King Meagre King.

125. ... This is your kinda place! Let's build the country right here!

126. What does your newborn country need to earn some respect in the global playground?

126.1. Oh, what a rush it was! Trying to work this stuff out.

126.1.1. Designing all the accoutrements your bantustan would need.

126.2. An anthem for starters.

126.2.1. A little tune to let everyone know you are coming.

126.2.2. It can't just be some sousa-band marching-time throw-off –

126.2.2.1. it has to work as ringtone too.

126.2.2.2. Be triumphant even when it sounds tinny.

126.2.2.2.1. And addictive.

126.2.2.2.1.1. Which means repetitive.

126.2.2.2.2. You take a tip from the advertising world.

126.2.2.2.3. A four note jingle.

126.2.2.2.3.1. Insanely catchy, memorable.

126.2.2.2.3.2. A proper earworm.

126.2.2.2.3.3. People will hear it and will not forget it.

126.2.2.2.3.4. Maybe Taylor Swift could sing it.

126.2.3. No lyrics though.

126.2.3.1. No words for footballers to stumble over before matches.

126.2.3.2. No odes to you reigning gloriously forever.

126.2.3.3. No hostages to fortune like that.

127. And then a passport. It can't be hard to make one of them.

> 127.1. A little notebook with some pink paper in it.

>> 127.1.1. But why does it even have to be that?

>>> 127.1.1.1. Let's mix it up! Let's burn the rulebook.

>>> 127.1.1.2. No biometric shit, no iris scanning, no barcodes, no machine readers.

> 127.2. Vouchers! Gift cards!

>> 127.2.1. Disposable loss leaders, guaranteed to get punters flocking in.

>> 127.2.2. Two-for-one entry into the country, and what the hell, you'll chuck in a chicken tikka masala too!

>>> 127.2.2.1 You can't say fairer than that can you, ladies and gentlemen?

128. Of course you like it.

> 128.1. Of course it is a stereotype.
>
>> 128.1.1. Shared common humanity on a plate.
>
> 128.2. But still, everyone likes it…
>
>> 128.2.1. don't they?

129. You have got tired of apologising for it.

> 129.1 Other people like baltis, vindaloos. Great. Good for them.
>
> 129.2. But why is it so hard for them to believe that you might not like that food?
>
> 129.3. You have got reconciled to the fact that you could never, still cannot, digest your mother's cooking.
>
>> 129.3.1. What can you do? Why are you rejecting it? Why is it rejecting you?
>
>> 129.3.2. You cannot help but take it as a metaphor.

130. Instead you sin against yourself, your heritage, your ancestry, by having steak.

130.1. Lots and lots of steak.

130.1.1. Or – you used to.

130.2. The nights you did, chow down on slabs of meat, gleaming with marbles of fat.

130.2.1. Those were the nights you could not sleep.

130.2.2. Night sweats.

130.2.3. Meat sweats.

130.2.4. And in your restless thrashings who do you see?

130.2.5. A god. The God.

130.2.5.1. Vishnu.

130.2.5.1.1. Smiling. Ever-smiling,

130.2.5.2. as he leans over you, sticks one of his many arms into your gut

130.2.5.3. and pulls out a lowing baby cow.

131. Happier thoughts, happier thoughts.

132. Self-promotion! A flag!

132.1. Of course, how could you be in any way a self-respecting nascent nation without a flag?

132.1.2. You do not want to be carrying someone else's banner.

132.2. This new thing should represent the fact that this country – your country – is good. And strong.

132.2.1. And will not be defined by its size, no sir.

133. There was a morning here, early on, when the sun was shining through whatever it is you have for curtains

133.1. an old post-sack you guess.

133.2. The sun did not do what you would expect it to,

133.2.1. stream in like it does in the clichés.

133.3. Instead it was focused, like someone had put a big magnifying glass in front of it.

133.3.1. And on the wall appeared an orange ball,

133.3.1.1. a synecdoche.

134. And at that moment, that little patch of wall was a synecdoche for what you were trying to do.

>134.1. It could have been Kerala. It could have been California.

>134.2. It could have been anywhere you go

>>134.2.1. to feel the awe of a sunrise.

>134.3. It could have been anywhere you go to dream.

135. You would have loved to have put that on the flag.

>135.1. But it would have looked a bit like Japan's old flag.

>135.2. And who wants to be associated with that bunch of imperial racists?

136. So what else could you use to brand your fledgling country?

> 136.1. What other symbol could you possibly appropriate for your own ends,
>
>> 136.1.1. paying tribute,
>>
>> 136.1.2. subverting what it stands for?
>
> 136.2. What could you hijack?
>
>> 136.2.1. Something you love.
>>
>> 136.2.2. Something you hate.

Another object now unfurls from the ceiling, obscuring the map. It is a giant Union Jack. Except that it is saffron and gold and red and brown and green in hue, vibrant and alive. There is an almost childish glee on his face as it unrolls.

137. Well, why not? It is mine as much as it is yours.

    137.1. You just thought it could be

        137.1.2. spiced up a little.

    137.2. It just needed a remix.

A breath, a break, a stop.

138. You loved your time under the Union Jack.

138.1. *Most* of your time under that flag.

138.1.1. That passport. That nationality.

138.2. You never got the sense it loved you back

138.2.1. in quite the same way.

139. You got that sense at the airport, mostly.

139.1. When you were stopped for the seventh

139.1.1. eighth

139.1.2. ninth

139.1.3. tenth

139.1.3.1. time in a row.

139.2. And of course, they are suggesting,

139.2.1. well, sorry about that,

139.2.1.1. we know *you* don't go in for that sort of thing,

139.2.1.2. that mid-air murdering sort of thing,

139.2.1.3. but the sad fact is that people who look a bit like you do.

139.2.2. So unfortunately

139.2.2.1. it's so unfortunate

139.2.3. but there you go, can't be too careful.

140. And you thought –

    140.1. *fuck that.*

    140.2. *You* can be too careful.

141. You cannot walk into an airport without breaking into a sweat.

    141.1. Which is, so you have been told, one of the signs

        141.1.1. of a terrorist.

    141.2. The steps taken to protect everyone

        141.2.1. including you

        141.2.2. end up compromising you.

    141.3. So much for sophisticated profiling.

        141.3.1. Does it take into account

            141.3.1.1. your lack of facial hair

            141.3.1.2. the pukkaness of your education

            141.3.1.3. your glottal stop

            141.3.1.4. your unasked for nationality?

    141.4. Apparently not.

    141.5. Which you will let go the first time

        141.5.1. the second time

        141.5.2. the third time.

    141.6. But the tenth?

    141.7. Then your profiling system is

        141.7.1. willful

        141.7.2. bullying

        141.7.3. fucked.

142. You put it this way.

>142.1. You are walking down the street

>>142.1.1. and you hear someone call you 'paki'.

>>142.1.2. (Don't gasp. It happens, it still happens

>>>142.1.2.1. even in places where you think it does not, could not.)

>>142.1.3. You let it go.

>>142.1.4. After all, you cannot be sure.

>>>142.1.4.1. You are on your own,

>>>142.1.4.2. you do not want the hassle,

>>>142.1.4.3. the trouble.

>142.2. Some time later, a few days,

>>142.2.1. a few weeks, a few months,

>>142.2.2. it happens again.

>>142.2.3. You walk on, again.

>142.3. Then it happens again.

>>142.3.1. And again.

>>>142.3.1.1. Five, six, seven, eight, nine times.

>142.4. And then it happens again.

143. And that tenth time, you turn round,

    143.1. you see who did it

        143.1.1. you go up to them, run up to them –

        143.1.2. blood rushing round your system like a train –

        143.1.3. and you put your face *this* close to theirs

            143.1.3.1. and you scream until you hit them.

                143.1.3.1.1. Or they hit you.

144. And God help you that is all it is. God help you if you are walking on your own on a dark street in a provincial town past midnight one night, and driving past you is a car filled with blokes, lagered up, leering, leaning out, screaming, 'PAAAAAAKKKKKKIIIIII!!!!', and the word hangs in the night, so harsh and audible you think you can start to see it forming in the mist that is starting to settle on you, all around you. And God help you because you suddenly realise you are on your own out here, and if they come back then what? You really are on your own out here, and what *was* that, do you think that was the screech of tyres in the middle of a handbrake turn, because one of them has realised that, hey, that one was on his own, this'll be easy, we can have some fun with this. And God help you when you run, because you will start running, you will run like you never have before, breathing in cloud and breathing out fear, your legs a cyclone as you try to get somewhere, anywhere, where you cannot be seen, cannot be found. And God help you that the door that you hammer on is unlocked, open, and you can dive inside it, slam it shut, and pull every lock in your favour, then slump down beside it, your lungs coming out of your mouth, your eyes coming out of your tears, praying to a god you don't believe in that no one knows you are here, can find you here.

144.1. And God help you too, when your luck finally does fail, and you get hit and you hit back, and someone calls the police, and you get an officer who actually believes you, does not think you are the one who has been winding people up, who backs you when you press charges, gets the wheels of justice turning, and you go to court and you tell people what happened, about how you were just walking, minding your business,

144.1.1. being a citizen,

144.2. and why can't you do this without being called names, and you were hit actually, and the people, the judicial people, go out and have a bit of a think, and whatever it is they do, come back and decide that the assault, your black eyes, your fear, are only worth a fine of £150.

144.2.1. Which does not even get fucking paid anyway.

The crown goes up in the air, against a wall. It bends out of shape.

145. You cannot ever forget being there was a test of endurance.

145.1. And you cannot ever forget that it was testing,

145.1.1. double, triple, a hundredfold,

145.2. for everyone who came before you.

145.3. The first generation.

145.3.1. The frontier, being on the edge –

145.3.1.1. that is always a crisis.

146. And the burden of expectations that was on them.

146.1. Making something of themselves.

146.2. Otherwise, why had they bothered moving?

146.3. There should always be a purpose to adventure.

147. And the burden of fitting in.

147.1. In a land of surprises they –

147.1.1. you –

147.1.2. could not afford to be more surprising

147.1.3. than they, your, colour already made you.

148. You landed in the mother country expecting,

>148.1. not milk and honey,

>148.2. but maybe tea and sympathy.

>148.3. Instead – beer, bronchitis and beatings.

149. And then the burden of choice.

>149.1. At some point, a choice is always placed in front of you.

>149.2. The choice.

>149.3. The choice your hosts always place in front of all guests.

>>149.3.1. Which master do you serve?

>149.4. When it comes to countries

>>149.4.1. you cannot split your loyalty, share your loyalty.

>>149.4.2. You can have two football teams, have two lovers.

>>>149.4.2.1. But you cannot have two nations.

>>>149.4.2.2. You can never love two countries

149.4.2.2.1. especially when your skin colour sticks out.

149.5. And so you are asked –

149.5.1. in pubs, in offices, in interrogation cells –

149.5.1.1. which master do you serve?

149.5.1.1.1. The one you say you do, on the passport we gave you?

149.5.1.1.2. Or the one your skin colour tells us you do?

150. You never get the answer right.

150.1. You never pass the exam.

151. Difference is more difficult to police than homogeneity, they say.

> 151.1. We've tried to let it flourish, they say –

>> 151.1.1. actively promoted it in fact –

> 151.2. let you have your cultures and your relative norms, they say,

> 151.3. your ways of speaking, your clothes, your funny-sounding music, funny-smelling food.

>> 151.3.1. And we've danced to it, worn it, eaten it –

> 151.4. we've fucked some of you, and enjoyed it –

152. But now we're in peril, they say,

> 152.1. because of what you believe,

>> 152.1.1. the words from your panoply of many-headed, many-armed gods –

>> 152.1.2. your warmongering jihadi god too.

> 152.2. And so all the funny-looking, funny-tasting stuff we enjoyed –

>> 152.2.1. those luscious, dark bodies we enjoyed –

> 152.3. these are all threats to us now, they say.

153. We don't understand you. How could we?

153.1. You're not like us. You never were like us.

153.1.1. You never will be like us.

153.2. So even if you say, you plead, you beg, you tell us – until the voice you use to call your fellows to prayer is as cracked and dry as one of your deserts – that you're loyal to us

153.2.1. we won't believe you.

153.2.2. We can't believe you.

153.2.3. We know you're not.

153.2.4. Deep down, we know you're not.

153.2.5. You never can be.

153.2.6. You weren't when we ruled your lands.

153.2.7. You forced us out, remember?

153.2.7.1. We remember alright. We don't forget.

153.2.7.2. And we know you've not changed.

154. You understand why they think that, think like that.

154.1. Still, the imperial mentality, the conquering mentality.

154.2. How long it takes to never die.

154.3. Made so much of the world red white and blue

154.3.1. they assume that is how the rest of the world thinks too.

154.4. Cannot begin to comprehend that they are not in danger of being taken over, overrun.

155. You – we – are here because you invited us.

> 155.1. For better or worse, landing on our shores, made us into a people,

> 155.2. made us a part of you at the same time.

> 155.3. Darker. But still a part.

156. And the burden of fitting in.

> 156.1. The efforts to fit in.

> 156.2. Not correcting people when they did not get your name right.

>> 156.2.1. Again. And again. And again.

> 156.3. You were polite. So you would fit in. And you did fit in.

> 156.4. But at the same time – you did not.

> 156.5. You conformed. And carried on.

> 156.6. You hid in full view.

157. But that isn't enough, they said.

>157.1. But how much more effort can you make?

>157.2. More effort, to hide the black feelings.

>>157.2.1. The white feelings.

>157.3. The bile.

>157.4. The contortions of thought, the hatred, that started to well up in you?

>157.5. The idea that death will be better than this.

>>157.5.1. That murdering your way to heaven is the only way to stop the pain now,

>>>157.5.1.1. the pain forever.

158. The Crown is off. Gloves off. Not today.

159. You had assumed it had got better.

>159.1. And it had got better.

>159.2. In some places. Some of the time.

160. But the assumptions, always the assumptions.

    160.1. No, you are from here.

    160.2. No, you were born here.

    160.3. No, you have not been.

        160.3.1. Sure, maybe, why not, no plans.

    160.4. No, you are not all friends.

    160.5. No, you do not all know each other.

    160.6. No, you are not an accountant.

    160.7. No, you are not a doctor.

    160.8. No, you are not a lawyer.

    160.9. No, you do not work in a corner shop.

        160.9.1. And your parents do not either.

    160.10. And no, you do not like Bollywood and you fucking hate curry.

161. Someone once told you there was a magic ratio.

161.1. Two to one.

161.1.1. Two of you to one of someone different.

161.2. No-one wants to be too outnumbered.

161.2.1. If people feel they are on the wrong side of the ratio, they will move, somewhere new.

161.2.2. The ratio will stay just about the same, so they are not, you know

161.2.2.1. 'being racist'.

161.2.3. They are being tolerant. Rational. Self-interested.

161.2.2.2. Self-segregating.

162. Some codes will always remain uncrackable.

162.1. Some doors always closed.

162.2. You cannot pick up a nationality just like that.

162.2.1. You just cannot.

162.2.2. Speaking English like an Englishman –

162.2.2.1. better than the English –

162.2.3. did you think that would be enough?

163. After a while you get tired.

163.1. Tired of the looks, open and not so.

163.2. The comments, just about loud enough

163.2.1. that you can catch the tail-end of them drifting away.

163.3. Tired of having to shave all the time,

163.3.1. in case anyone thinks that your beard

163.3.1.1. is just that bit too long.

163.3.1.1.1. As if anyone could be bothered to unpick the differences between someone with religion and someone without.

163.3.1.1.2. We are all the same; just one big mass of darkies, coming to build our minarets, put your women in burkas, then blow you up.

164. So when a country, which in its own imagination

    164.1. is one of the most tolerant places on the planet,

    164.2. turns out to be less tolerant than its imaginings,

    164.3. where do you go?

    164.4. If you cannot hide in a city, a metropolis which has evolved to absorb every creed and colour,

        166.4.1. where do you go?

165. And if you are not at home in the place you were born,

    165.1. and you cannot go back to the place your parents came from,

        165.1.1. as you did not come from there,

    165.2. where do you go?

166. Your imagined country.

    166.1. Did you think it would be enough?

    166.2. Of course this is an imagined country.

        166.2.1. Every country is imaginary.

            166.2.1.1. Collective fallacies in a sea of flags.

167. You have done everything to try and fit in.

167.1. Speak the language, not your parents'.

167.2. Eat the food, not your parents'.

167.3. Supported the fucking cricket team.

167.3.1. And all for what?

167.4. When something happens, when some moment of pressure arrives, someone,

167.4.1. lots of someones,

167.5. turn round and say:

167.5.1. 'Where do you come from? We don't ask it idly. We only ask it of people who we think won't provide a satisfactory answer. Do you really think a passport matters? Do you really think being born here matters? Do you really think it's that easy to belong? Do you think 300 years of ownership provided us with any duty of care?'

168. No, not care.

>168.1. Only control.

>168.2. The majority must have its way.

>168.3. You must fit in with its ways.

>168.4. And still it is not enough.

169. Your state is not enough.

170. There are no minorities in your state.

>170.1. There are no majorities in your state.

>>170.1.1. Therefore there is no misfortune in your state.

>>>170.1.1.1. And you will march into your rightful place alongside destiny.

STOP.

WE ARE INVADING YOUR COUNTRY.
WE ARE INVADING YOUR COUNTRY.
IT IS TOO LATE FOR YOU. WE ARE
INVADING YOUR COUNTRY. LEAVE
EVERYTHING. TAKE NOTHING.

STOP. STOP. STOP.

171. You get it. You are out of time.

    171.1. Game over.

172. Your parents chose pain then.

    172.1. You choose pain now.

    172.2. You choose freedom.

        172.2.1. You choose the freedom to escape easy categorisation.

        172.2.2. To escape the stereotyping that others make of you.

    172.3. You choose to reinvent yourself

        172.3.1. as something that you know you could never be.

173. You will not have being foreign thrust upon you.

    173.1. You are going to embrace it yourself.

    173.2. This grass, this land you have made for yourself, isn't greener, could never be greener.

        173.2.1. But it is yours. For now.

A shell lands. An explosion expands. An impassive response, unfazed.

174. You never had much patience with people who asked

> 174.1. 'Where are you from?'

> 174.2. Because when somebody asks you that

>> 174.2.1. you know they will not accept the answer: 'Here'.

>> 174.2.2. It can never be here, for people who ask that question.

>> 174.2.3. They will keep tracing it back and back and back.

>> 174.2.4. Until there is a reason to exclude you.

175. But here is the truth.

> 175.1. You are a mongrel nation.

>> 175.1.1. *We are a mongrel nation.*

> 175.2. A bunch of Germans and Spainards and Danes and Celts and Gauls rattling around in a pot.

>> 175.2.1. What's a few more colours thrown in to spice things up?

176. Yes, the island's story is proud –

176.1. perched, with back turned, all defiant, on somebody else's shore.

176.2. Daring them to come in.

176.2.1. And for 1,000 years and more, the jewel has been protected.

176.3. But remember: invasion-free does not mean purity.

176.3.1. The acorn of their family was planted somewhere else.

176.3.2. They just happened to fall here, sprout here, bed-in here.

176.3.2.1. And then they tore down the oak to make the fence to try and keep your tribe out.

176.3.2.2. Even though their father's father's father's father was a black-skinned ghost too.

177. We are all from somewhere else.

177.1. Some people just hide it better than others.

178. You were not searching for a utopia.

178.1. Just a place you fit.

178.2. But you did become a king.

179. And soon you will not have to worry about the hallucinations any more.

    179.1. Seeing skeletons.

    179.2. Whiter-than toothpaste-white

        179.2.1. rising out of the ground.

    179.3. But before they really start to come after you,

        179.3.1. they stop and clean themselves off.

        179.3.2. They make sure all the soil and the dirt,

            179.3.2.1. all the black and the brown,

        179.3.3. are wiped off their bones before they start coming for you.

180. You are pleased to matter.

    180.1. Matter to something.

    180.2. Even if it does not exist.

    180.3. Even if it never did.

181. You are not an island.

> 181.1. You are an empire.

> 181.2. You are an empire, or you are nothing.

> 181.3. Within your own borders, you shall be accepted for who you are.

A last silence.

182. It is not about megalomania. It is about survival.

183. Your reality is a dream. This reality is a dream. Everyone's reality is a dream. So why not make those dreams crazy, wondrous, unique, superlative, awe-inspiring, jaw-dropping, impossible? Why not dream of something you really want to be real? How else do you find out what is true?

184. You have got to stop lying to yourself.

    184.1. No crown but truth.

185. You never understood why you would fight –

    185.1. die –

        185.1.1. to defend a place.

    185.2. Sing songs, improvise weapons, crawl through sewers.

        185.2.1. It is just some streets, is it not?

            185.2.1.1. If they want them that badly, they can have them.

186. Now you get it.

187. You are without the country you started in. You will finish in the country you started.

188. And will you pick up a shovel, to start digging your own green and pleasant land?

> 188.1. Nations are not lucky collections of soil and flesh, blessed by a smiling God.
>
> > 188.1.1. They are as much an invention as the wheel, as jelly beans.
> >
> > 188.1.2. A confection, an eighteenth-century accident invented by press barons and generals.

189. And if you are waiting for a moral, do not. You wish you could say that all of this has been driven by something higher, something profound. A thirst for power. An even more rampaging ego. Here, now, cornered, you can finally see that you have been lying to yourself. What has been driving you on has been nothing noble. It has been vanity. Venal vanity, vicious vanity.

190. Step outside yourself. Make a new story. A better one.

190.1. What matters is what works.

190.2. What counts is what survives.

190.3. And what changes is everything.

191. You did not create this to light a path for others, or build a shining city on a hill. To be a guideland. You did it so that you could feel you were the hero of your own story. That people would look at you once, then more than once, if you had a crown on your head. And they did. But you did not realise that people would want to rip it off, this glittering affirmation of who you are, from the top of your head. Vanity is not useless. It has made you what you are. The hollow wreck that you are. You forgot that this place should have stayed a no-place. Should have stayed a crazy idea on a train. Metaphysics versus geography, and you lost. You forgot that people are protective of what they have. That they rarely like unannounced strangers turning up in their midst, and turning one of their back gardens into a personal Zion. You forgot that the better argument rarely wins out against the better gun. Or any gun. It is only because you were not welcome there that you are here.

192. And if you are waiting for a moral, do not.

> 192.1. And if you are waiting for a moral, do not.

>> 192.1.1. And if you are waiting for a moral, do not.

193. All the sun and the cool kids are next door. They always will be.

> 193.1. You will hold on to no memories.

>> 193.1.1. Except one.

>> 193.1.2. That all dreams should end suddenly.

>> 193.1.3. The best ones always do.

In a small room, a border of masking tape. A demarcation down the middle.

The litter of a temporary kingdom: a mattress, a desk. A TV, a lamp, a rucksack.

Stretched out, a body. Blue torso and yellow legs, bandaged in combat trousers and vest, desert boots. No crown.

He lies, the head resting bloody. Alarm clock gunfire and explosive sunset don't scramble him awake.

Good riddance tramper! Here's a loudhailer with your leaving papers!

WE HAVE INVADED YOUR COUNTRY.

STOP.

Notes and Acknowledgements

Saffron Jack started as a response to two BLDG BLOG posts: about The Akwizgran Discrepancy (http://www.bldgblog. com/2008/07/the-akwizgran-discrepancy/), and a town in Belguim, Baarle-Hertog: http://www.bldgblog.com/2008/07/ baarle-hertog/.

At various points in its writing I was also helped by *The Rough Guide to Micronations*, Ionesco's *Exit The King*, Rudyard Kipling's novella *The Man Who Would Be King*, and the 1975 film adaptation, directed by John Huston and starring Michael Caine and Sean Connery; a transcribed quotation (with deliberate errors) from the latter is on page 42.

The form of the poem is inspired and informed by Mónica de la Torre's 'How to Look at Mexican Highways'. My thanks to her for inspiring Jack to find his form. You can read Mónica's wonderful poem at: https://www. poetryfoundation.org/poems/53885/how-to-look-at-mexican-highways

The thrilling cover for the book is by Ria Dastidar.

With thanks to: Daljit Nagra, who despite seeing Jack in all his previous, less attractive incarnations, never lost his belief in him; Mona Arshi, Luke Kennard and Nathalie Teitler for kind words at the right time; Khairani Barokka, who saved Jack from some of his more egregious errors; Dave Coates for sage advice and excellent pop knowledge; Françoise Walot for saving my blushes in French and Flemish; Jane Commane, as ever, for taking the chance; Mum, Dad and Ria; and Marie.